The Pot of Gold

an Irish folk tale

D1315216

SCOTT, FORESMAN AND COMPANY • GLENVIEW, ILLINOIS
Dallas, Tex. • Oakland, N.J. • Palo Alto, Cal. • Tucker, Ga. • Brighton, England

ISBN 0-673-10620-9

Once upon a time there was a mean man named Grumble.

One day Grumble saw an elf in the woods.
Grumble said, "An elf always has
a pot of gold.
I'll make this elf take
me to his pot of gold."

Grumble took hold of the elf.

The elf began to jerk this way and
that way.
But Grumble didn't let go.

The elf said, "Let me go! Let me go!"

Grumble said, "Take me to your
pot of gold.
Then I'll let you go."

The elf took Grumble to a big tree.
The elf said, "The gold is under this tree.
You'll have to dig deep to get it."

Grumble said, "I'll need a shovel
to dig with.
I'll go home and get one.
But first I'll mark the tree so I can
find it again."

Grumble took off his red scarf and put it
on a branch of the tree.

He said, "Now promise you won't take my scarf off the tree."

The elf said, "I promise."

Grumble let the elf go.

Then Grumble ran home to get a shovel.

Grumble said, "Now all I have to do is
dig up the gold, and I'll be rich."

When Grumble got back, he looked for
the tree that had his red scarf on it.

The elf had kept his promise.

He had not taken Grumble's scarf
off the tree.

He had put a red scarf on every tree.

Grumble began to yell and scream and
stamp his feet.
But that didn't help at all.

So he began to dig, and he may still
be digging.

8 9 10 11 12 13 14 RRD 98 97 96 95 94 93

1. How did the elf fool Grumble?

2. Why did the elf fool Grumble?